MAIN IDEA

Written by **Shannon Keeley**

Illustrated by **Ethan Long**

Flash Kids
A division of Spark Publishing
NEW YORK

This book belongs to

_____

Executive Editor: Hanna Otero
Managing Editor: Vincent Janoski
Graphic Designer: April Ward
Editor: Eliza Berkowitz

This edition published by Spark Publishing

Spark Publishing
A Division of SparkNotes LLC
120 Fifth Avenue, 8th Floor
New York, NY 10011

ISBN 1-4114-0021-6

Please send all comments and questions or report errors to www.sparknotes.com/errors

Printed in China

Dear Parent,

Understanding the main idea of a reading passage is an important skill your child needs to succeed at reading. This book will help your child learn how to read critically and identify the main point of the material. It includes lots of high-interest reading passages on diverse topics, and the level of difficulty increases as the book progresses. To get the most from the activities included here, follow these simple steps:

- Find a comfortable place where you and your child can work quietly together.
- Encourage your child to go at his or her own pace.
- Help your child read the words and sentences.
- Offer lots of praise and support.
- Let your child reward his or her work with the included stickers.
- Most of all, remember that learning should be fun! Take time to look at the pictures, laugh at the funny characters, and enjoy this special time spent together.

A Quiet Ghost Town

Read the passage and think about the main idea.

A ghost town tells us about the past. A ghost town is a place where people lived many years ago. The people are gone, but some of the old buildings are still there. You might see an old water well or horse stable, but you won't see any ghosts!

Read each question and circle the correct answer.

1. The topic of the passage is:

    a) ghost towns

    b) ghosts on Halloween

    c) ghost costumes

2. Another good title for this passage would be:

    a) How to Make a Ghost Town

    b) Ghost Towns: Life in the Past

    c) Ghost Towns and Haunted Houses

3. The main idea of the passage is:

    a) In the past, people never went to ghost towns.

    b) Ghost towns show us what life was like years ago.

    c) You will find lots of ghosts in a ghost town.

Many Flavors of Honey

Read the passage and think about the main idea.

Not all honey tastes the same. This is because bees use flower nectar to make honey. The flavor depends on what type of flower the bee used. Some honey tastes like clovers. Honey can also taste like orange blossoms. There are as many flavors of honey as there are types of flowers!

Read each sentence in the chart. Decide if the sentence is the main idea of the passage or a detail. Put a check in the correct column.

Sentence	Main Idea	Detail
1. Bees use flower nectar to make honey.		
2. The flavor of honey depends on what type of flower the bee used.		
3. Some honey tastes like clovers.		
4. Honey can also taste like orange blossoms.		
5. There are as many flavors of honey as there are types of flowers!		

Reading Puzzle

Read the passage and think about the main idea.

Today, people listen to the radio to hear music or news. Years ago, people listened to the radio to hear stories. This was before people had television sets. Radio shows used actors to act out stories. Some shows were funny, while others were serious. Radio shows were like television shows without pictures!

Find the puzzle piece with the best title for the story.
Then find the puzzle piece with the main idea of the story.
Draw a line to connect the two puzzle pieces.

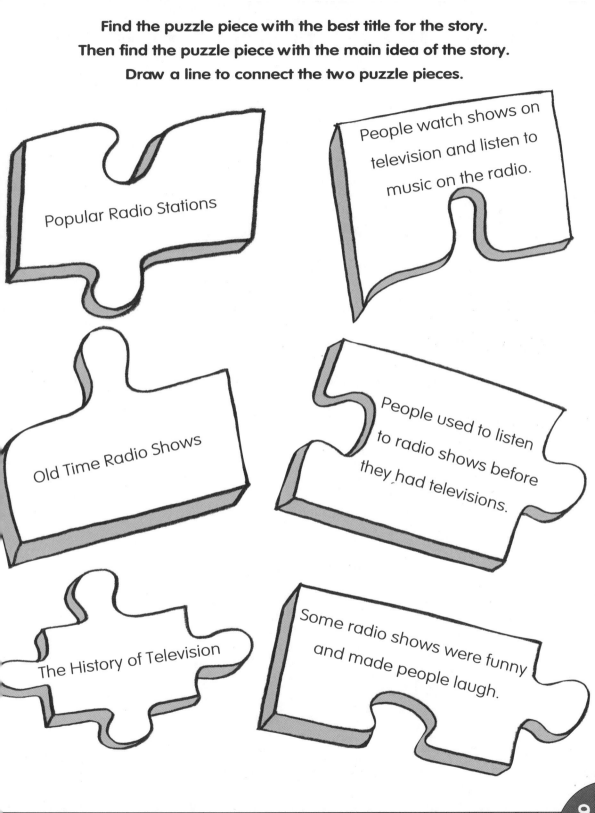

Popular Radio Stations

People watch shows on television and listen to music on the radio.

Old Time Radio Shows

People used to listen to radio shows before they had televisions.

The History of Television

Some radio shows were funny and made people laugh.

The City and the Country

Read the passage and think about the main idea.

There are good things about living in the city and the country. Living in the city is exciting. There are lots of people and fun things to do. The city is busy and interesting. Living in the country is relaxing. The country is quiet and peaceful. You can go hiking and enjoy the outdoors. Both the city and the country are good places to live!

Using the sentences at the bottom of the page, write the main idea that goes with the sentences in each box. In the middle box, write the main idea that tells about both groups of sentences.

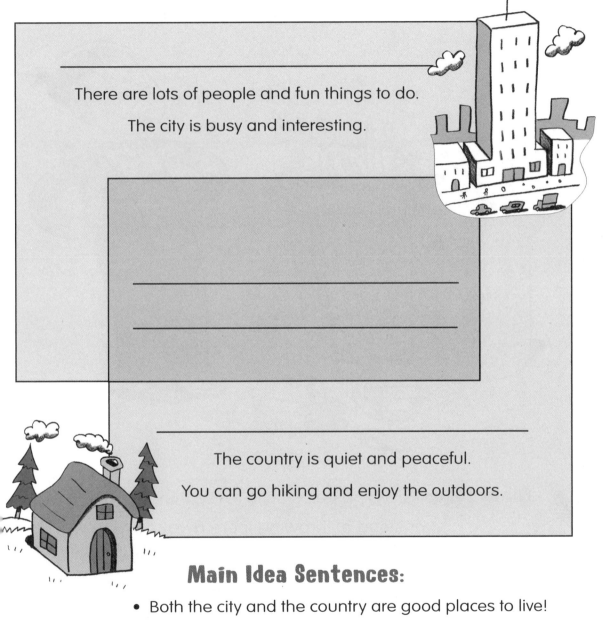

_____

There are lots of people and fun things to do.

The city is busy and interesting.

_____

_____

_____

The country is quiet and peaceful.

You can go hiking and enjoy the outdoors.

Main Idea Sentences:

- Both the city and the country are good places to live!
- Living in the country is relaxing.
- Living in the city is exciting.

Recycling

Read each main idea and the sentences beneath it.
Cross out the sentence that does not go with the main idea.

Main Idea: Recycling helps us to reuse things
instead of throwing them away.

1. Throwing everything away creates too much trash.
2. It's important to take the trash out every day.
3. There is no place to keep all the trash, so we need to recycle!

Main Idea: One thing you can recycle is paper.

1. White paper can be turned into notebook paper.

2. Then, notebook paper can be recycled to make newspaper.

3. Always keep plenty of paper in your notebook.

Main Idea: You can also recycle plastic.

1. You can buy soda in plastic or glass bottles.

2. You can put plastic bottles into a recycling bin.

3. The bin is taken to a factory so the plastic can be reused!

Read and Write

Read the passage and think about the main idea.

My Playful Pet Dog

I like my pet dog because he is playful. If I throw a ball, my dog runs to get it. My dog enjoys going for walks and running in the park. My dog has lots of energy and is always ready to play. He is a lot of fun!

**Read the passage. Think of a good title
for the passage, and write it on the line.**

Title: _____

    I like my pet bird because he is funny. I can teach my pet bird to say funny things. My bird makes funny noises and flaps his wings. He really makes me laugh!

**Read the passage. Think of a good title and write it on the title line.
Then think of a sentence that gives the main idea.
Write it on the line at the beginning of the passage.**

Title: _____

_____

My pet cat enjoys sitting quietly on my lap. She likes to purr softly. My cat curls up next to me for a nap. She is a nice, quiet friend.

April Fool's Day

Read the passage and think about the main idea.

Playing jokes on April Fool's Day is an old tradition. It started in France. People used to celebrate New Year's Day on April 1. Then, they changed the calendar, and New Year's moved to January 1. But some people still celebrated the New Year on April 1. They were called "April fools." April 1 became a day for tricks and pranks.

Read each question and circle the correct answer.

1. The topic of the passage is:

    a) April Fool's Day

    b) New Year's Eve

    c) April weather

2. Another good title for this passage would be:

    a) The History of April Fool's Day

    b) Great April Fool's Day Tricks

    c) Staying Safe on April Fool's Day

3. The main idea of the passage is:

    a) Everyone plays jokes on January 1 to celebrate New Year's Day.

    b) People in France still celebrate the New Year on April 1.

    c) April Fool's pranks started when the date of New Year changed.

Meg's Birthday Surprise

Read the passage and think about the main idea.

Meg's ninth birthday was a day full of surprises. In the morning, Meg's brother brought her breakfast in bed. In the evening, Meg's mom made a special dinner. Then Meg's dad brought a big cake box to the table. Meg opened the box, but there wasn't a cake inside. A puppy jumped out! Meg went to bed very happy. Everyone had planned something special for her birthday.

Read each sentence in the chart. Decide if the sentence is the main idea of the passage or a detail. Put a check in the correct column.

Sentence	Main Idea	Detail
1. In the morning, Meg's brother brought her breakfast in bed.		
2. Then Meg's dad brought a big cake box to the table.		
3. Everyone had planned something special for her birthday.		
4. A puppy jumped out!		
5. Meg's ninth birthday was a day full of surprises.		

Reading Puzzle

Climbing Mt. McKinley, the highest peak in the United States, is a big challenge. About 1,000 people try to climb Mt. McKinley each year. Only about half of them make it to the top. The climb can take from fourteen days to five weeks. Climbers spend eight to ten hours a day climbing, and the weather is very cold. It's no wonder that Mt. McKinley is called "Denali" in the local language. Denali means "the high one," and its peak is 20,320 feet high!

Find the puzzle piece with the best title for the story.
Then find the puzzle piece with the main idea of the story.
Draw a line to connect the two puzzle pieces.

Climbing Mt. McKinley

The local name for Mt. McKinley is "Denali," which means "the high one."

The History of Denali

Climbing to the top of Mt. McKinley is a long, hard challenge.

Where to Camp on Mt. McKinley

About 1,000 climbers make it to the top of Mt. McKinley each year.

The Naming of French Fries

Read the passage and think about the main idea.

How did French fries get their name? People disagree about the story of French fries. Some people say that the idea for fried potatoes started in France and Belgium. People in France and Belgium speak French. So, in America, people named them "French fries." Other people think that French fries get their name from their shape. To "french" a piece of food is to cut it into a long strip. So, "frenched" potato strips make "French fries." Nobody knows the real reason behind the name French fries, but we enjoy eating them anyway!

Using the sentences at the bottom of the page, write the main idea that goes with the sentences in each box. In the middle box, write the main idea that tells about both groups of sentences.

_____

_____

_____

People in France and Belgium speak French.

So, in America, people named them "French fries."

_____

_____

_____

_____

_____

To "french" a piece of food is to cut it into a long strip.

So, "frenched" potato strips make "French fries."

Main Idea Sentences:

- People disagree about the story of French fries.
- Other people think that French fries get their name from their shape.
- Some people say that the idea for fried potatoes started in France and Belgium.

The Land of the Midnight Sun

Read each main idea and the sentences beneath it.
Cross out the sentence that does not go with the main idea.

Main Idea: In some parts of the word, the sun never goes down during the summer.

1. Because these places are so far north, the sun points at them all summer.

2. Summer activities include swimming, hiking, and fishing.

3. We call these places "The Land of the Midnight Sun."

Read each question and circle the correct answer.

1. The story tells mostly about:

    a) finishing homework on time

    b) looking for a lost dog

    c) finding lost homework

2. Another good title for this story would be:

    a) How I Found My Lost Homework

    b) The Day I Forgot My Homework

    c) The Lost Dog Ate My Homework

3. The main idea of the story is:

    a) The narrator helped his neighbor find a lost dog.

    b) The narrator was very upset about losing his homework.

    c) The narrator put up a flyer to help find his lost homework.

Susan B. Anthony: American Hero

Read the passage and think about the main idea.

Susan B. Anthony is an important American woman. During the 1800s, women did not have the right to vote. Susan B. Anthony was upset about this and felt it was unfair. In 1872, she decided to vote in an election. It was against the law for women to vote, so she was fined. Even so, this was a big step in helping women gain more rights. Her courage helped women get the right to vote.

Read each sentence in the chart. Decide if the sentence is the main idea of the passage or a detail. Put a check in the correct column.

Sentence	Main Idea	Detail
1. Susan B. Anthony is an important American woman.		
2. In 1872, she decided to vote in an election.		
3. Susan B. Anthony was upset about this and felt it was unfair.		
4. Susan B. Anthony's courage helped women get the right to vote.		
5. During the 1800s, women did not have the right to vote.		

Reading Puzzle

Read the passage and think about the main idea.

   Have you ever wondered why ducks float on top of the water? Most living things have to swim to stay afloat. Even floating on your back takes some effort. But ducks seem to float without even trying. How do they do it? Ducks are covered with oily feathers. Oil is lighter than water. If you pour oil in a glass of water, the oil floats on top. So, the duck's oily feathers make it float on top of the water!

Find the puzzle piece with the best title for the story.
Then find the puzzle piece with the main idea of the story.
Draw a line to connect the two puzzle pieces.

How Fast Do Ducks Swim?

Ducks like to float in ponds and lakes.

How Do Ducks Float on Water?

Ducks float because the oil in their feathers is lighter than water.

How Many Feathers Do Ducks Have?

Ducks can float without even trying, unlike other living things.

Ice-Skating and Roller-Skating

Read the passage and think about the main idea.

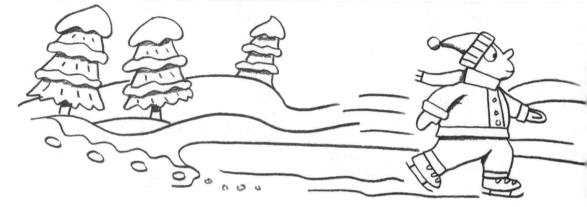

Ice-skating and roller-skating both require a lot of balance. When you ice-skate, you wear shoes with sharp blades and glide along the ice. The blades are very thin, so keeping your balance is tricky. When you roller-skate, you wear shoes with rolling wheels. The wheels are very small, so it's easy to lose your balance. You have to be careful not to roll too fast while you are learning to skate.

Using the sentences at the bottom of the page, write the main idea that goes with the sentences in each box. In the middle box, write the main idea that tells about both groups of sentences.

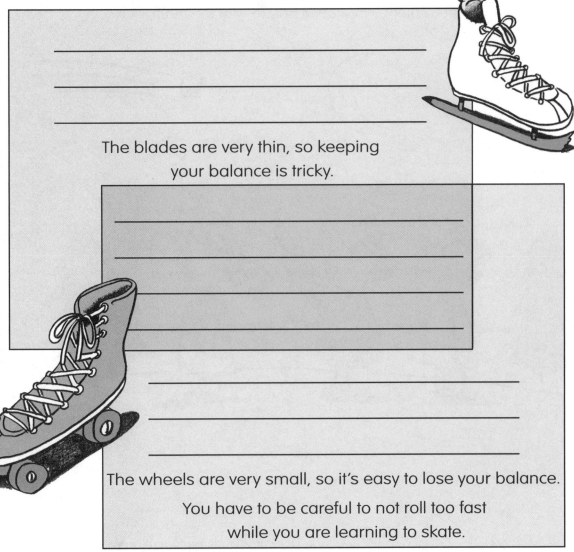

_____

_____

_____

The blades are very thin, so keeping your balance is tricky.

_____

_____

_____

_____

_____

_____

The wheels are very small, so it's easy to lose your balance.

You have to be careful to not roll too fast while you are learning to skate.

Main Idea Sentences:

- When you roller-skate, you wear shoes with rolling wheels.
- Ice-skating and roller-skating both require a lot of balance.
- When you ice-skate, you wear shoes with sharp blades and glide along the ice.

Comets

Read each main idea and the sentences beneath it. Cross out the sentence that does not go with the main idea.

Main Idea: A comet looks like a splash of moving light in the sky.

1. The sun is the largest star in our solar system.
2. Comets are actually made up of gas, ice, and dust.
3. Comets travel around the sun in an orbit.

Main Idea: Comets get warmer as they get closer to the sun.

1. The sun makes the head of the comet start to melt.
2. This melting gives the comet a long, flowing tail of gas and dust.
3. Some people think comets bring bad luck.

Main Idea: A comet is usually named after the person who discovered it.

1. You need a powerful telescope to see a comet.
2. Halley's Comet was named after Edmond Halley.
3. Hale-Bopp Comet was named after Alan Hale and Thomas Bopp in 1995.

Read and Write

Read the passage and think about the main idea.

How Birds Survive Winter

During the cold winter months, birds need a warm place to live. So, most birds fly south. Many birds travel in large flocks for safety. They use the sun, moon, and stars to find their way. Many birds fly to the same place every winter. Birds are able to find more food in the south during the winter. When winter is over, they fly north again.

**Read the passage. Think of a good title
for the passage, and write it on the line.**

Title: _____

During the cold winter months, bears need a warm place to live. So, they find a warm cave and go into a deep sleep. Their heartbeats and breathing slow down. Because of this, bears use very little energy while they sleep. When the winter is over, they wake up.

**Read the passage. Think of a good title and write it on the title line.
Then think of a sentence that gives the main idea.
Write it on the line at the beginning of the passage.**

Title: _____

_____

_____

Most turtles and frogs move to the very bottom of the pond. They bury themselves under leaves or in the mud. They rest on the bottom of the pond until winter is over. When it gets warmer, they come out of the water.

Transportation

Read the passage and think about the main idea.

Every day, children all over the world have to get to school. However, not all kids get there in the same way! Many children walk to school or ride bikes. If they live too far away, kids might take the bus or ride in a car. In places with lots of snow, kids might use a snowmobile or skis to get to school. Children who live on islands might need to take a boat or ferry. Children use all kinds of transportation to get to school!

Read each question and circle the correct answer.

1. The topic of the passage is:

    a) how children get to school

    b) school buses

    c) getting to school on time

2. Another good title for this passage would be:

    a) How to Ride a Ferry to School

    b) Different Ways of Getting to School

    c) The School Carpool

3. The main idea of the passage is:

    a) Depending on where they live, children
       get to school in different ways.

    b) Children who take the bus get to school
       faster than those who walk.

    c) Some kids live too far away from the school
       to walk or ride a bike.

Celebrating Earth Day

Read the passage and think about the main idea.

Earth Day is a special day to think about how to take better care of our planet. We celebrate Earth Day on April 22. There are lots of ways to celebrate Earth Day. Some people like to plant a new tree. Others might help pick up trash to keep a park clean. Some cities have special fairs to teach people about the Earth. Earth Day is a time to learn more about helping the Earth, and to have fun too!

Read each sentence in the chart. Decide if the sentence is the main idea of the passage or a detail. Put a check in the correct column.

Sentence	Main Idea	Detail
1. Some people like to plant a new tree.		
2. Earth Day is a special day to think about how to take better care of our planet.		
3. There are lots of ways to celebrate Earth Day.		
4. Some cities have special fairs to teach people about the Earth.		
5. Earth Day is a time to learn more about helping the Earth, and to have fun too!		

Reading Puzzle

Read the passage and think about the main idea.

Making dinner for a family takes a lot of work. Dana learned this the hard way. Usually, Dana's sister helped make dinner, and Dana washed all the dishes. But one night, Dana switched jobs with her sister. Dana helped wash and chop vegetables for the salad. She tried to drain the noodles, but she dropped them in the sink. To make matters worse, the tomato sauce didn't taste right. It was a disaster! Dana decided that helping with dinner was too much work. She would rather wash the dishes!

Find the puzzle piece with the best title for the story.
Then find the puzzle piece with the main idea of the story.
Draw a line to connect the two puzzle pieces.

Dana and the Dishes

Dana learned that making dinner is a lot of hard work.

Dana's Dinner Disaster

Dana decided that she didn't want to wash the dishes anymore.

Dana's Favorite Dinner

Dana realized that the tomato sauce didn't taste right.

Two Kinds of Currents

Read the passage and think about the main idea.

Sometimes, a word can have more than one meaning. The word "current" has two very different meanings. "Current" can be used as an adjective. It can describe something happening in the present time. You might read the current issue of a magazine or wear a current style of clothing. The word "current" can also be a noun. Used this way, "current" refers to movement in a body of water. When you swim in a stream, you will feel the flow of the current. The word "current" may seem simple, but its meanings are very different!

Using the sentences at the bottom of the page, write the main idea that goes with the sentences in each box. In the middle box, write the main idea that tells about both groups of sentences.

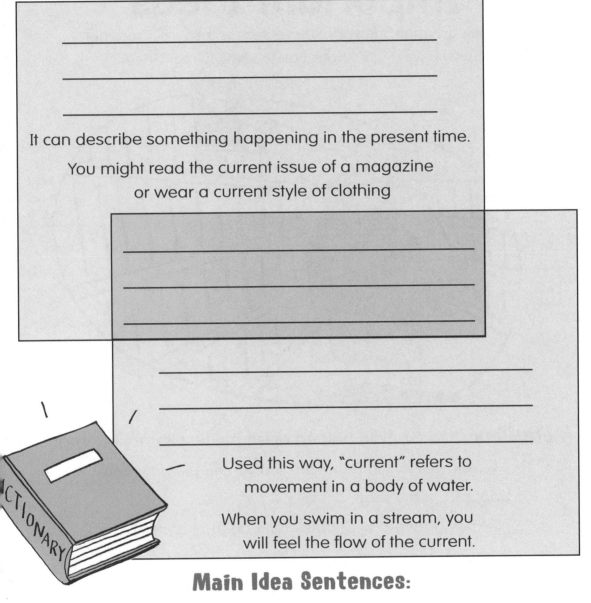

_____

_____

_____

It can describe something happening in the present time.

You might read the current issue of a magazine or wear a current style of clothing

_____

_____

_____

_____

_____

_____

Used this way, "current" refers to movement in a body of water.

When you swim in a stream, you will feel the flow of the current.

Main Idea Sentences:

- The word "current" has two very different meanings.
- "Current" can be used as an adjective.
- The word "current" can also be a noun.

Ben Franklin's Important Ideas

Read each main idea and the sentences below it. Cross out the sentence that does not go with the main idea.

Main Idea: Ben Franklin helped open the first library in America.

1. It was important to Ben Franklin that people buy more books from his shop.

2. He knew that many people could not buy books because they were expensive.

3. So, he bought books for a library, where people could come and borrow them.

4. Franklin's library inspired other towns to open libraries as well.

Main Idea: Ben Franklin also liked to experiment and invent new things.

1. While experimenting with a kite during a storm, Franklin learned about electricity.
2. His experiment proved that lightening is actually a form of electricity.
3. Franklin retired from the printing business at the age of 42.
4. Then, Franklin invented a lightening rod to keep buildings and ships safe in storms.

Main Idea: Ben Franklin was an important leader to the American people.

1. Franklin created a wood stove which people still call the "Franklin stove."
2. Franklin helped America gain freedom from England.
3. After the war was over, Franklin helped make a peace treaty with England.
4. Then, he helped make laws to set up our new country.

Read and Write

Read the passage and think about the main idea.

A Painter's Tools

A painter uses many tools to create a painting. Painters use many different kinds of paint. Some paints are light and soft, like watercolors. Others are bright and bold, like oil paints. Painters also use different kinds of surfaces. They might paint on special paper, or on a thick canvas. They might paint on a wall, or even on the sidewalk. To get the paint onto the surface, painters use brushes. Brushes can be big, thick, small, or thin. A painter knows how to use these tools to paint his or her artwork.

Read the passage. Think of a good title for the passage, and write it on the line.

Title: _____

A sculptor uses many tools to create a sculpture. Some sculptors begin with a large piece of rock. They use special knives and picks to chip away at the rock. They carve the rock into a shape. Sculptors can also work with clay. At first, the clay is wet and soft. Sculptors can mold it with their hands. Then the clay dries and gets hard. A sculptor uses these tools to sculpt his or her artwork.

Read the passage. Think of a good title and write it on the title line. Then think of a sentence that gives the main idea. Write it on the line at the beginning of the passage.

Title: _____

_____

Some quilters use a large wooden frame to hold the fabric. They call it a "quilting frame." Quilters use small squares of different fabric. They sew the squares together with special needles and thread. Quilters can stuff the inside of the blanket with batting to make it thick. Some quilters make fancy designs on the fabric. Quilters know how to use these tools to sew a quilted piece of artwork.

Native American History

Read the passage and think about the main idea.

Chief Joseph was an important Native American leader. He was chief of the Nez Perce tribe. His tribe was a peaceful tribe. At first, Chief Joseph helped his tribe get along with the white settlers. But in 1877, the settlers tried to force the Nez Perce tribe off their land. Though he opposed war, Chief Joseph fought for his people and their land. They lost the battle, but he was still a hero to his tribe. Chief Joseph always spoke out for the rights of Native Americans. People remember him as a brave and wise leader.

1. The topic of the passage is:

    a) white settlers

    b) Chief Joseph

    c) Chief Nez Perce

2. Another good title for this passage would be:

    a) Nez Perce Traditions

    b) Chief Joseph's Speech

    c) Chief Joseph: Wise Leader

3. The main idea of the passage is:

    a) Chief Joseph was a strong leader who helped fight for Native American rights.

    b) Chief Joseph did not win the battle for his tribe's land.

    c) The Nez Perce tribe was peaceful and got along with the white settlers.

Weather Watchers

Read the passage and think about the main idea.

    Meteorologists are scientists who study the weather. They can tell us about the weather before it happens. This is called a weather forecast. Weather forecasts help us get ready for the weather. We listen to forecasts to find out if we need warm clothes or an umbrella. Sailors use weather forecasts to stay away from storms at sea. Pilots need weather forecasts to figure out the safest way to fly. Even farmers listen to weather forecasts to plan for their crops. By forecasting the weather, meteorologists make our lives safer and easier!

Read each sentence in the chart. Decide if the sentence is the main idea of the passage or a detail. Put a check in the correct column.

Sentence	Main Idea	Detail
1. We listen to forecasts to find out if we need warm clothes or an umbrella.		
2. Weather forecasts help us get ready for the weather.		
3. Sailors use weather forecasts to stay away from storms at sea.		
4. By forecasting the weather, meteorologists make our lives safer and easier!		
5. Pilots need weather forecasts to figure out the safest way to fly.		

Reading Puzzle

Read the passage and think about the main idea.

The people of ancient Greece created many kinds of art. They wrote long poems about their gods and heroes. Sometimes they made statues of these heroes. They also created paintings called "frescoes." To make a fresco, they painted on wet plaster. Greek artists glued small pieces of stone, glass, and gold onto walls or floors to form pictures called mosaics. Some Greek artists made beautiful pottery. You can see ancient Greek vases in museums. The artists of ancient Greece had many talents. They loved creating beautiful art in different ways.

Find the puzzle piece with the best title for the story.
Then find the puzzle piece with the main idea of the story.
Draw a line to connect the two puzzle pieces.

Greek Poets and Writers

Artists in ancient Greece created poems, statues, frescoes, mosaics, and vases.

Art Museums in Ancient Greece

Glass vases made by artists in ancient Greece can be seen today in museums.

The Art of Ancient Greece

Greek artists often made art in honor of their gods and heroes.

The Xylophone and the Drums

Read the passage and think about the main idea.

The xylophone and the drum both belong to the same family of instruments, called the percussion family. People play percussion instruments by striking them. The xylophone is played by striking bars with a special stick called a mallet. Each bar gives the sound of a different note. By striking the bars in a certain order, you can create songs. The drum is played by striking its surface with a stick or with your hand. The drum makes a sound like a stomp or thud. By striking the drum in a pattern, you can create a beat. The xylophone and the drum are both in the same family, but they make very different sounds!

Using the sentences at the bottom of the page, write the main idea that goes with the sentences in each box. In the middle box, write the main idea that tells about both groups of sentences.

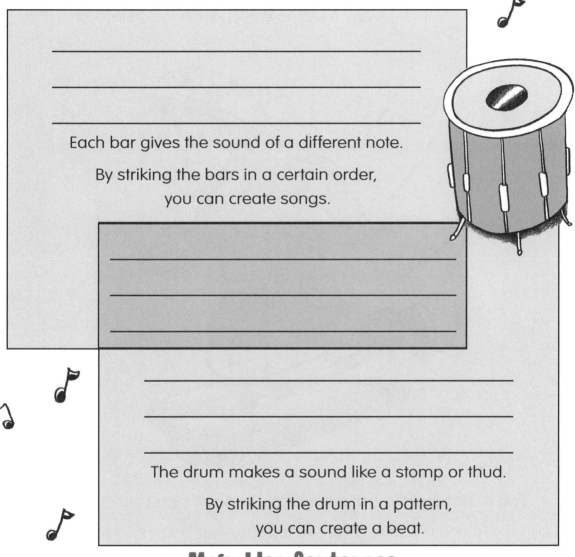

_____

_____

_____

Each bar gives the sound of a different note.

By striking the bars in a certain order,
you can create songs.

_____

_____

_____

_____

_____

_____

The drum makes a sound like a stomp or thud.

By striking the drum in a pattern,
you can create a beat.

Main Idea Sentences:

- The drum is played by striking its surface with a stick or your hand.

- The xylophone is played by striking bars with a special stick called a mallet.

- The xylophone and the drum are in the same family,
  but they make very different sounds!

Super Skateboard

Read each main idea and the sentences below it.
Cross out the sentence that does not go with the main idea.

Main Idea: Riding a skateboard is good exercise.

1. To ride a skateboard, you must push off with your legs.

2. All that pushing makes your legs strong.

3. Some skateboard tricks include jumping, which is also good exercise.

4. Riding a skateboard will help you get to school more quickly.

Main Idea: A skateboard is also a good way to get places quickly.

1. Riding a skateboard is a lot faster than walking.

2. Riding a skateboard would teach me good balance.

3. On a skateboard, I can travel a long way without getting tired.

4. I could ride my skateboard to school, and I would never be late!

Main Idea: Skateboards are also a safe way to have fun.

1. There is a skateboard park down the street that is very safe.

2. No skateboard tricks are allowed at the park, so I won't get hurt.

3. I can wear a helmet and kneepads in case I fall off the skateboard.

4. During the summer, the skateboard park gets really crowded.

Answer Key

Page 5
1. a
2. b
3. b

Page 7
1. detail
2. detail
3. detail
4. detail
5. main idea

Page 9
Old Time Radio Shows + People used to listen to radio shows before they had televisions.

Page 11
Top box:
Living in the city is exciting.

Middle box:
Both the city and the country are good places to live!

Bottom box:
Living in the country is relaxing.

Page 12
Paragraph 1:
Cross out sentence 2.

Page 13
Paragraph 1:
Cross out sentence 3.
Paragraph 2:
Cross out sentence 1.

Page 15
Answers will vary.

Page 17
1. a
2. a
3. c

Page 19
1. detail
2. detail
3. detail

4. detail
5. main idea

Page 21
Climbing Mt. McKinley + Climbing to the top of Mt. McKinley is a long, hard challenge.

Page 23
Top box:
Some people say that the idea for fried potatoes started in France and Belgium.

Middle box:
People disagree about the story of French fries.

Bottom box:
Other people think that French fries get their name from their shape.

Page 24
Paragraph 1:
Cross out sentence 2.
Page 25
Paragraph 1:
Cross out sentence 2.
Paragraph 2:
Cross out sentence 1.

Page 27
Answers will vary.

Page 29
1. c
2. a
3. c

Page 31
1. main idea
2. detail
3. detail
4. detail
5. detail

Page 33
How Do Ducks Float on Water? + Ducks float because the oil in their feathers is lighter than water.

Page 35
Top box:
When you ice-skate, you wear shoes with sharp blades and glide along the ice.

Middle box:
Ice-skating and roller-skating both require a lot of balance.

Bottom box:
When you roller-skate, you wear shoes with rolling wheels.

Page 36
Paragraph 1:
Cross out sentence 1.

Page 37
Paragraph 1:
Cross out sentence 3.
Paragraph 2:
Cross out sentence 1.

Page 39
Answers will vary.

Page 41
1. a
2. b
3. a

Page 43
1. detail
2. main idea
3. detail
4. detail
5. detail

Page 45
Dana's Dinner Disaster + Dana learned that making dinner is a lot of hard work.

Page 47
Top box:
"Current" can be used as an adjective.

Middle box:
The word "current" has two very different meanings.

Bottom box:
The word "current" can also be a noun.

Page 48
Paragraph 1: Cross out sentence 1

Page 49
Paragraph 1:
Cross out sentence 3.
Paragraph 2:
Cross out sentence 1.

Page 51
Answers will vary.

Page 53
1. b
2. c
3. a

Page 55
1. detail
2. detail
3. detail
4. main idea
5. detail

Page 57
The Art of Ancient Greece + Artists in ancient Greece created poems, statues, frescoes, mosaics, and vases.

Page 59
Top box:
The xylophone is played by striking bars with a special stick called a mallet.

Middle box:
The xylophone and the drum are in the same family, but they make very different sounds!

Bottom box:
The drum is played by striking its surface with a stick or your hand.

Page 60:
Paragraph 1:
Cross out sentence 4.

Page 61:
Paragraph 1:
Cross out sentence 2.
Paragraph 2:
Cross out sentence 4.

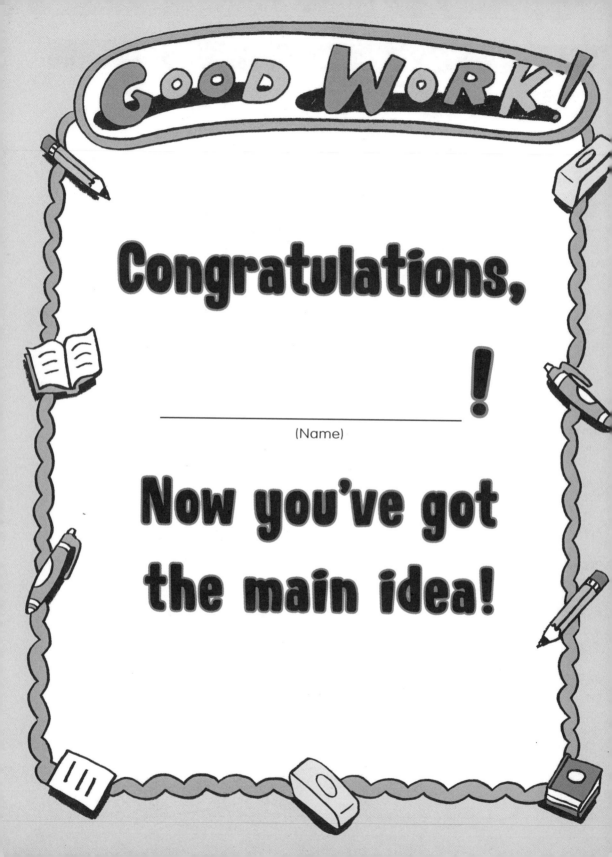

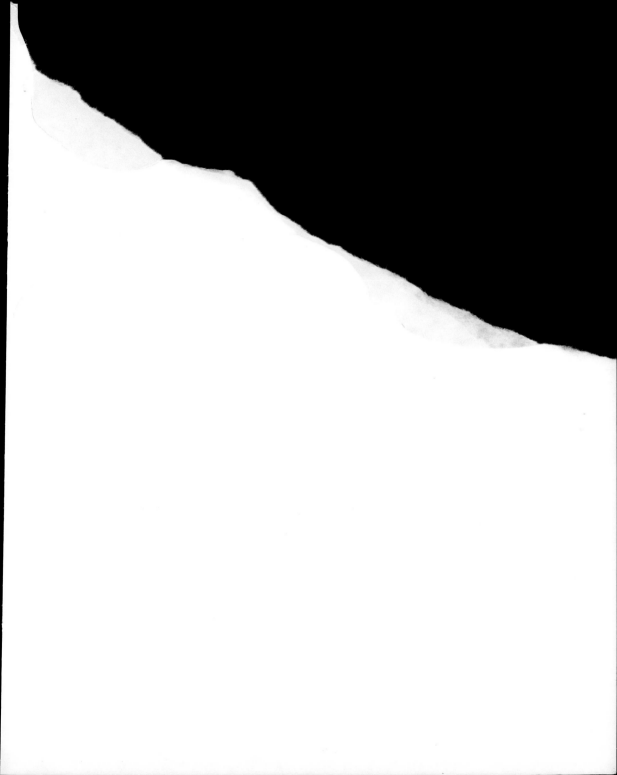

SUPER!

Flash Kids
LEARNING IN A FLASH